High Shelf

High Shelf XXVIII. March 2021.
Portland, Oregon.

ISBN: 978-1-952869-28-0

Cover Image by Yaara Rozner Laizé
Design, Layout and Editing by C. M. Tollefson

With special thanks to:
David Seung, Kelsey Beck Kuther, Megan Kim, & River Elizabeth Hall.

High Shelf XVIII

March 2021

"...We will be held in captivity,
while sheep roam the unpeopled village streets.

We will sit, scrounge, stockpile, stake out a living, sanitize.
We will surrender to the foreign country we've become.
We will be strangers to strangeness... "

Charise M. Hoge

"... So he's asleep now, dreaming among
the martyred souls—
the martyred souls who showed us
how important it is to love our own..."

Thomas Kneeland

Table Of Contents

Void

C. Hiatt O'Connor

It might not be fair to call it that
since it can be distilled into trillions, quintillions,
with light as time and colors all --

what a void really is is absence
yet there you are, here with us, without walls
in the endless more --

so, bar us and light and birds and green and snow and so on
ad infinitum, you might be able to call it that.
I don't mean to condescend.

What I really mean is, there is no consolation
from a thing absent of will. That is,
if the white eyes of Ursae Majori

aren't joints of some cosmic skeleton
who paws across a placeless place without direction,
but are only nuclear spheres, white with a reaction

other than rage.
What else do we have
but our common peculiarity of circumstance?

Well, nothing, bar us and light and birds and green and snow
and so on, *ad infinitum*.

Recurring

Madeline Ewanyshyn

#1

I wander

a beach I've never been to,

approach a pier

cloaked in fog.

An uneasy sky,

leads me -lost

and barefooted-

along the damp grey sand,

which shifts beneath me,

becoming something wild

I cannot name.

Looking back, it's the static between TV channels

An acrid scent-

burnt toast?

tells me it's

time to leave.

So I remove

my feet, and

walk away.

#2

I am losing

my precious teeth.

They are spilling out

like so many opals-

more riches than

I can spend,

and I am left

to mourn

with the taste of iron

in my mouth.

Alternatively:

The teeth escape

and crawl

down my throat.

I cough and cough,

but

I cannot open myself up

to release.

On Leaving in the Living Season

Cleo Lockhart

I want growth to fill every crevice of this place;
let roots pierce the floorboards and bring me down through them
to a shallow terracotta grave
and let them make themselves a home here
in my place.

Fruits hanging heavy from the ceiling fan,
flowers choking up the pipes. In dreams,

my room is filled with insects, but in truth
they are better suited to the space than I
and adept at taking back what they can devour.
There is no throne higher

than that of the decomposer, for they are the things that feast
on all that once feasted — I want them
covering the walls and making the world shake, consuming
as they were meant to consume,

making away with everything
but the foundations,
all save for the skeleton. I want them
to feed what grows. In the meantime

give me a tender burial — what is a body
if not a home — and let the sunlight reach
what craves it.

American Dream

Yaara Rozner Laizé

Coca-Cola

Coca-Cola

American
DREAM

Д/ТОП.

문화예술회관
청소년수련관
YOUTH CENTER
시립박물관

BILARDO
BILARD

BILARDO
BILARDO

Art in an Age of Uncertainty

Charise M. Hoge

for Joshua Miller

Theatre-in-the-round, Shakespeare in the Park,
opening night, live concert will be cancelled.

Premiere, bookstore reading, arts festival, gallery show,
museum exhibit, new release will be cancelled.

The readers, actors, dancers,
visual artists, musicians will stay home.

The paintings will not be viewed. The poetry will not be spoken.
The dance will not be staged. The music will not be heard.

We will wear masks, without costumes.
Grocery stores will have lines, without tickets.
Health care workers will be given applause, without reservation.

We will be held in captivity,
while sheep roam the unpeopled village streets.

We will sit, scrounge, stockpile, stake out a living, sanitize.
We will surrender to the foreign country we've become.
We will be strangers to strangeness.

Spacing will be six feet apart in public, and in private we will pace
... to and from doorways, up or down staircases, around furniture.

Forward momentum will loop back, with more curves in each path.
The Golden Ratio will restring the musician's instrument

and arch the dancer's back. The sculptor will render a sunflower
from the whirlpool effect. And the poet will extract black ink
from the center of our spiraling.

BELLE-ÎLE

Stelios Mormoris

Thistle shoots collect in the strata
of the dark cliffs, layered
like fine long plates of mica.
The sky flattened on the sea offered

such solace from a distance,
two merging tableaux that made us wince
as silverness unfolded into golden,
and we submitted like children

to hold hands, re-avow, despite
our eyes slit by the horizon,
where flirted out of sight
the terrible birds of our derision.

Form, Figures, Hell

Phoebe Greer

FORM
On a train
Sitting with Jean Rhys
Looking out
The open doors
we are *vendeuse*, we see
leaves spiral in air

VESSEL
A slow blink
For miles, cloud drift
Across sun
Blue volvo
Dry arranged eyelashes
Long Island Pine Bar-
rens

CONNEXS
Hitting up
my mom for info
On her CBD
Supplier
Comfortably-numb.net
Do they ship to NY?

HOMESCHOOL
I believe
That speaking kindly
Forces nice
Of the mouth
Nice-ness is a flower
Sarah's Moon Carrot

TOKEN
Last year went:
Bad bad really bad
Really good
Good bad bad
Saw dolphins at Fort Tilden
Good OK ok

HELL
Driving a car
That doesn't break properly
Cursed Cherry blossoms
What it's like
To not think about
How I look

SPORT
Brendan said
He couldn't tell if
My poems
Are entries
Into my cute diary
Monday April, Tenth

SNOW DAY
Haunted by
An ancestral bride
The log pile
Hegalian
Marrying the rainy days
Cum I won't swallow

FIGURES
Let it down
Spring feeling it
The wisteria
Back of bus
Hairdryer sized vibrator
Grapes from the fridge

Quarantine Dreams

Bill Schulz

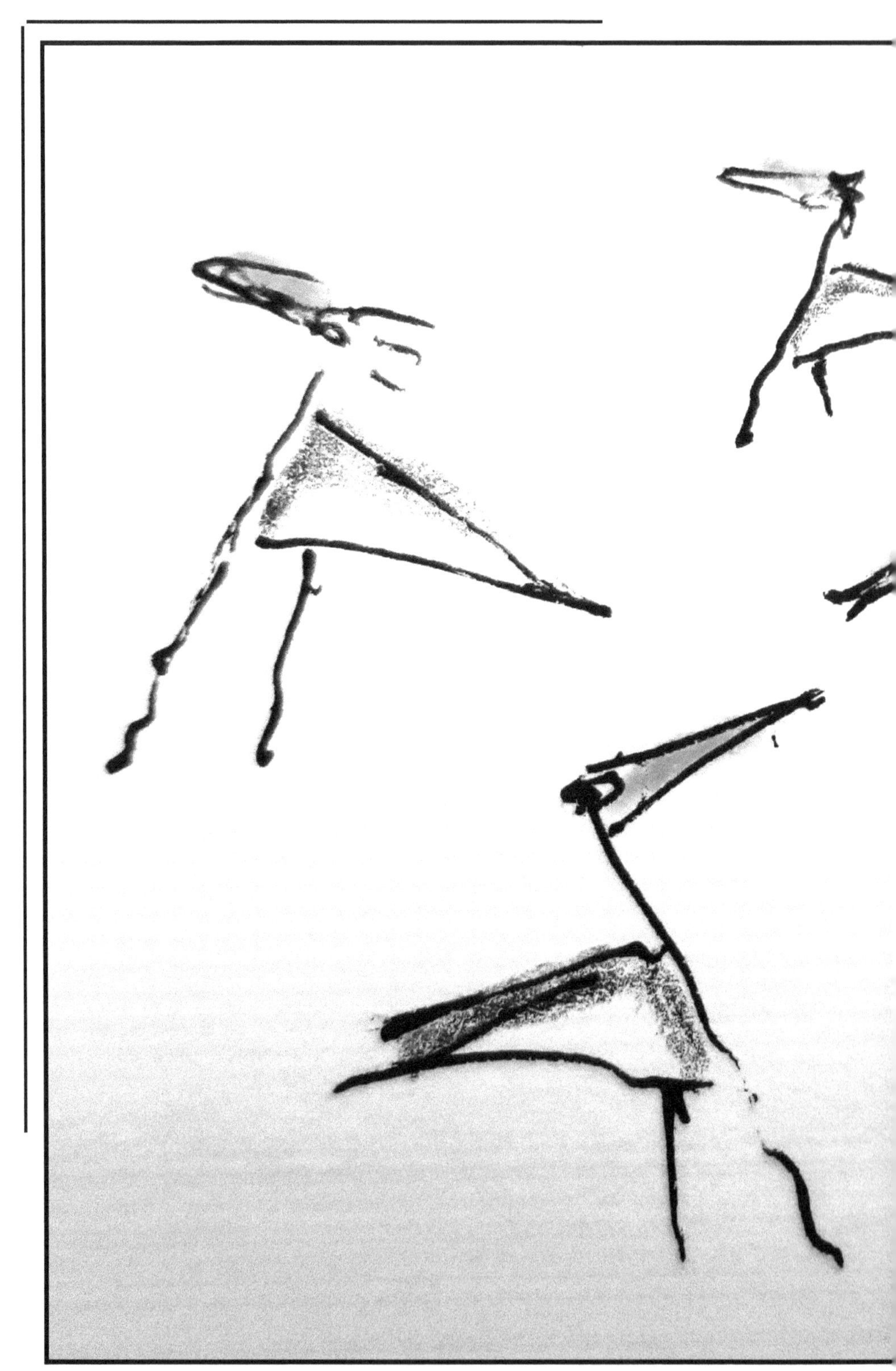

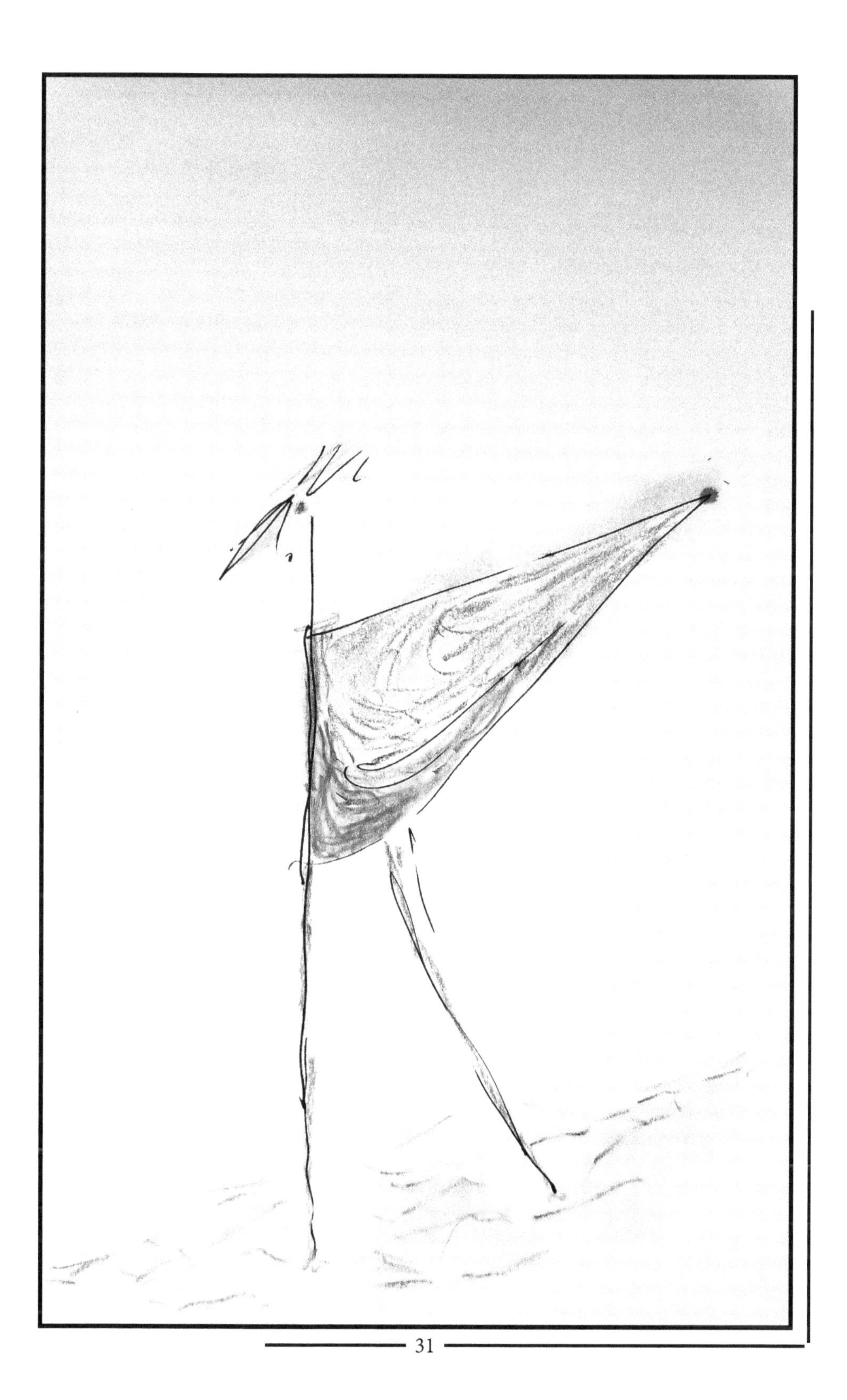

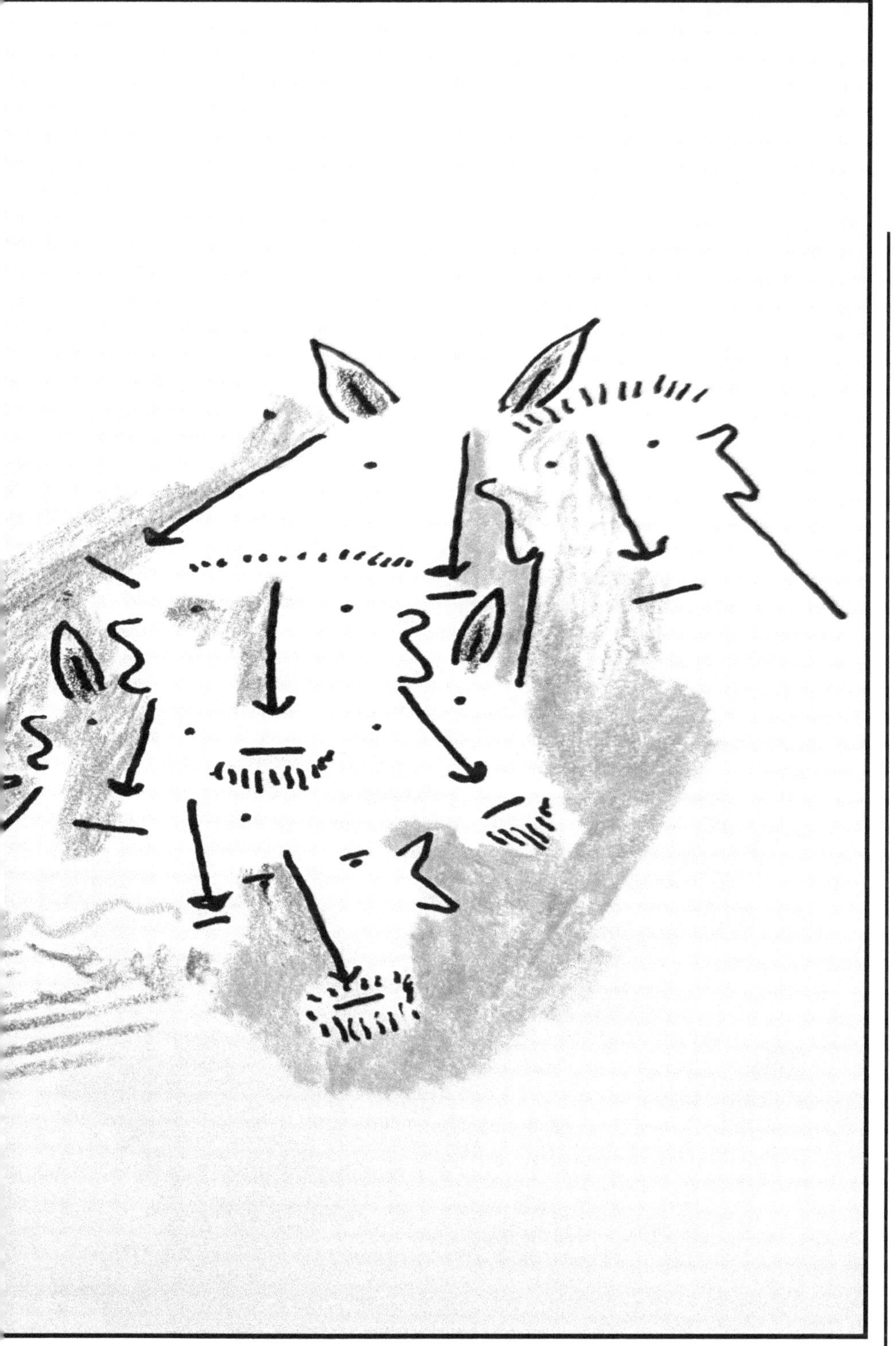

Stillborn

Gwen Bernick

& I remember being born:
fruit bloomed in the night,
shadowed and ripe and golden,
the wet fold of some womb
that a flashlight could tear
straight through, bright red skin
from spine to tattered naval.

Unbeing in the morning,
the light fractured across
the counter, fruit rotted right there
in white ceramic, blinds drawn,
& mom always yelling,
& the car always running.
I want to drift across
till I don't feel my skin
like a warm, wet wall
around my wicked head.
I want to sleep in the bathtub
with my face under the spout
and my skull cracked open,
pouring, pouring.
I want to make it up as I go along.
I want to wash my body apart,
to hold my mind hostage inside of me
until it dissolves into blood
beneath my heart-beating kidneys.
I think this is what the world looks like
when you're not trying to be anything.
Whole and ugly and cheated. Scraping
plaque off of your teeth on the bus.

& so I drink my coffee through a little straw
to burn my mouth a little slower, to feel it
fill my body like a wet bag of red flesh.

But I remember being born,
my skin tender and pink and fresh,
the arms of the enemy
cradling my mean, fragile head
against her calloused breast.
& here I am wandering, here I am alone.

How I reconcile freedom and flowering,
the gasping breath of autonomy
like a jailbird from my comfortable,
miserable body, my tailpipe throat,
stillborn every day I awake.
My own calloused chest, my
selfish lungs filled
with thick, grey exhaust,
the cars running and running.
I am riding the bus through the morning,
being human
and insignificant. Being the kitchen
floor, the breadth of hatred folded
into the muffled, wet womb of silence.
But I was sitting there
in my folded cotton sheets,
like a normal kid,
flashlight to my palm
'cause I liked to see it
shine all the way through.

Mad Girl's Love Song

Catherine LeComte

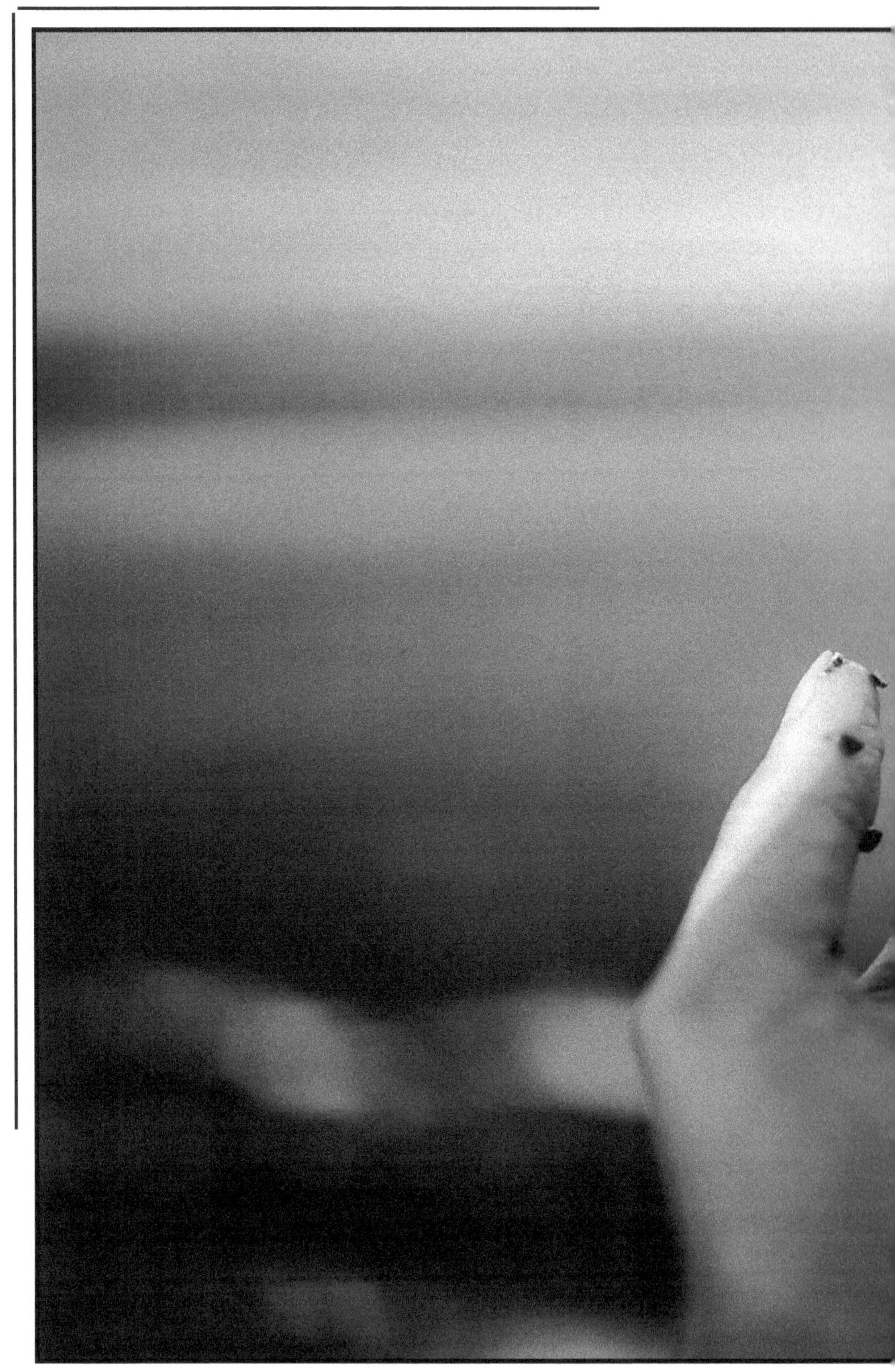

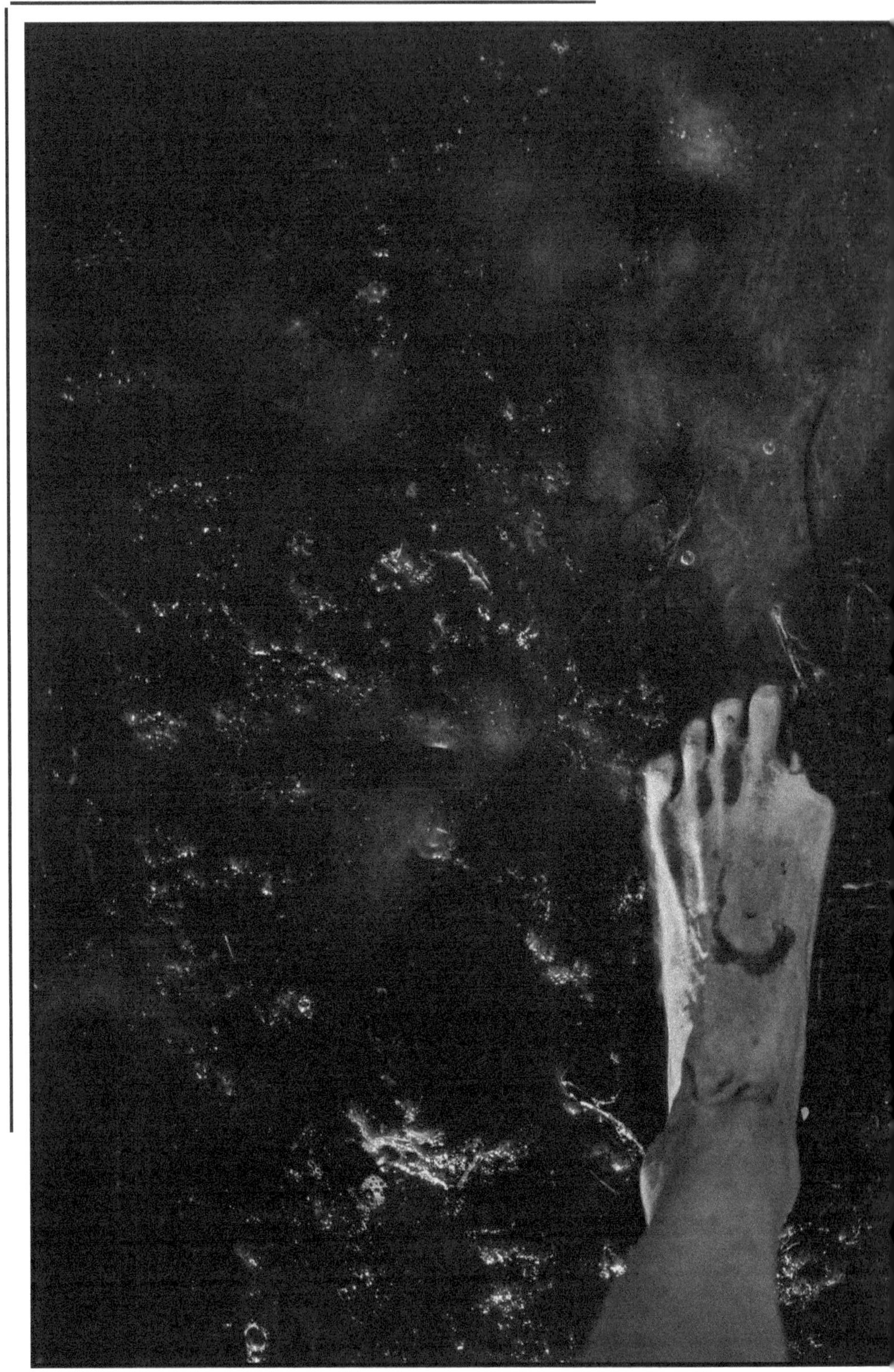

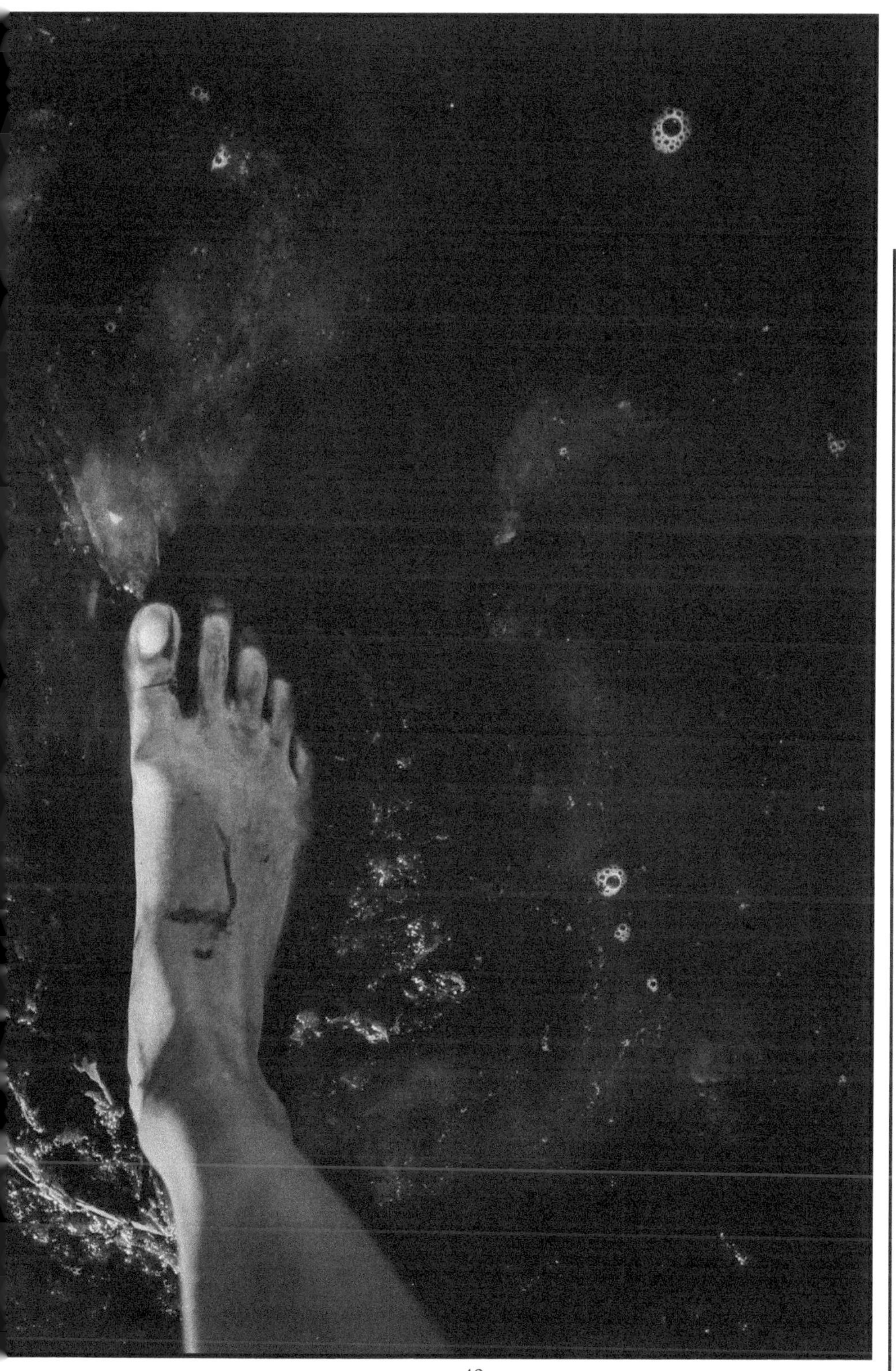

Intuition of Origin

Jessica Bidwell

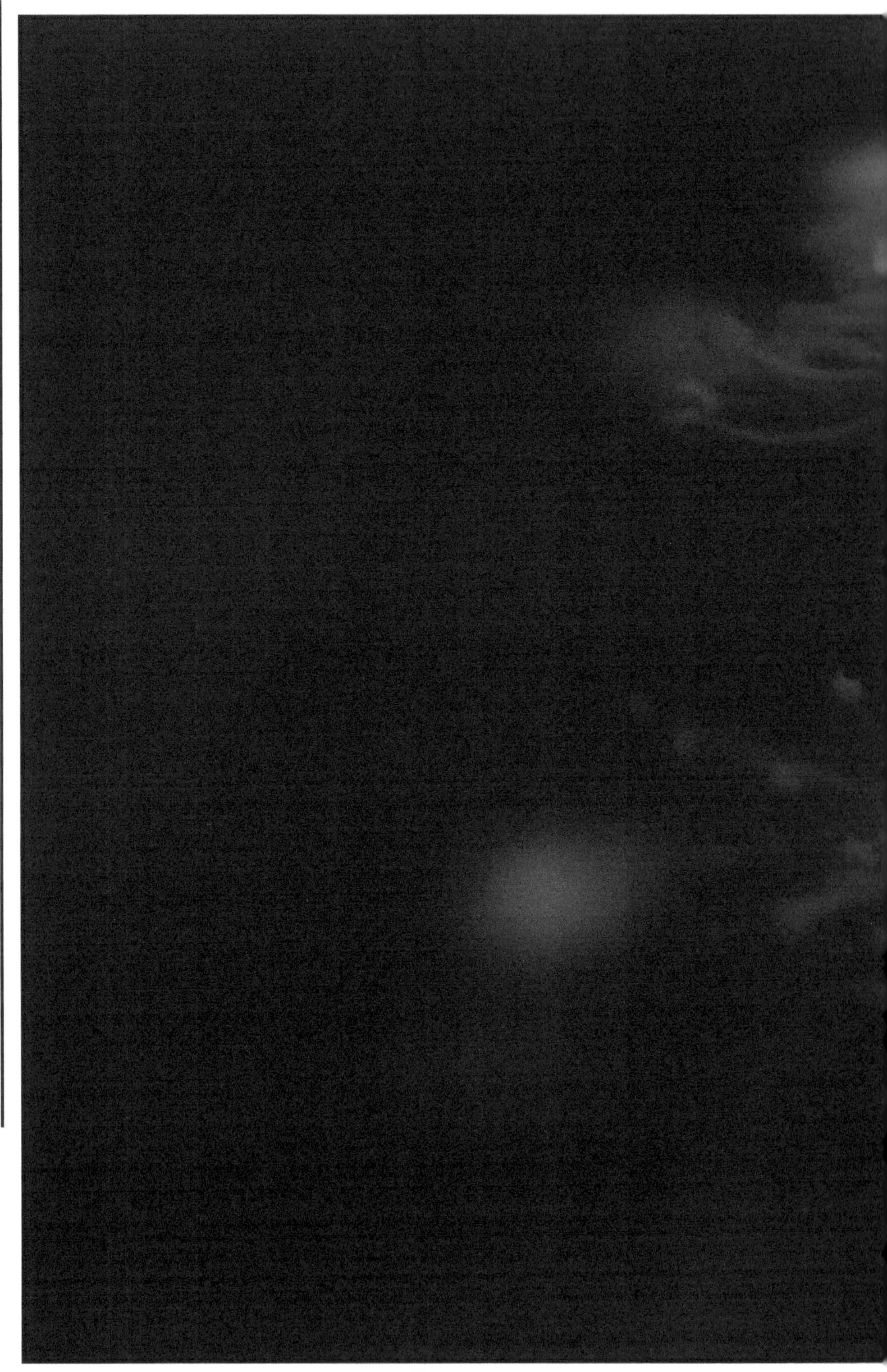

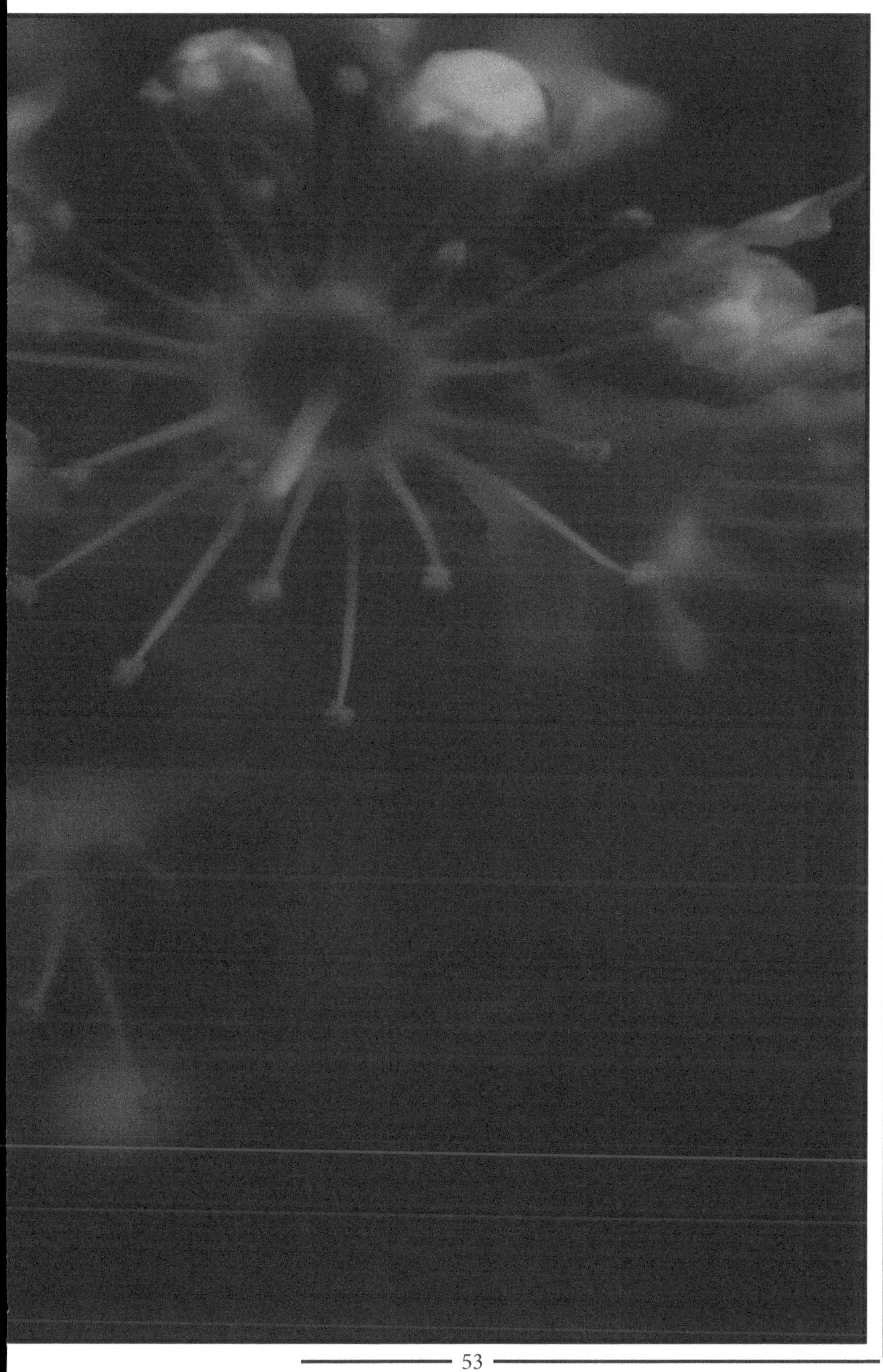

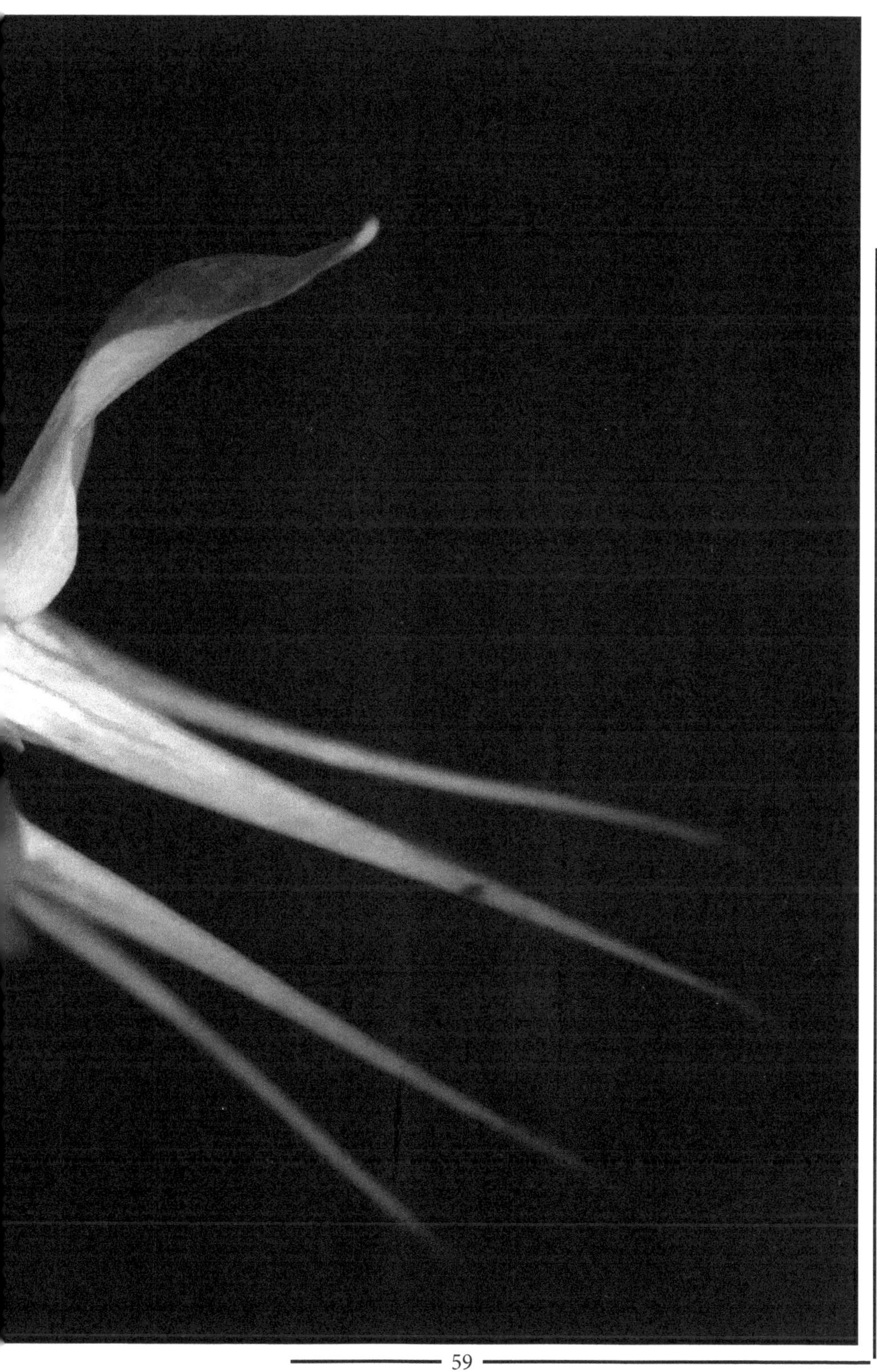

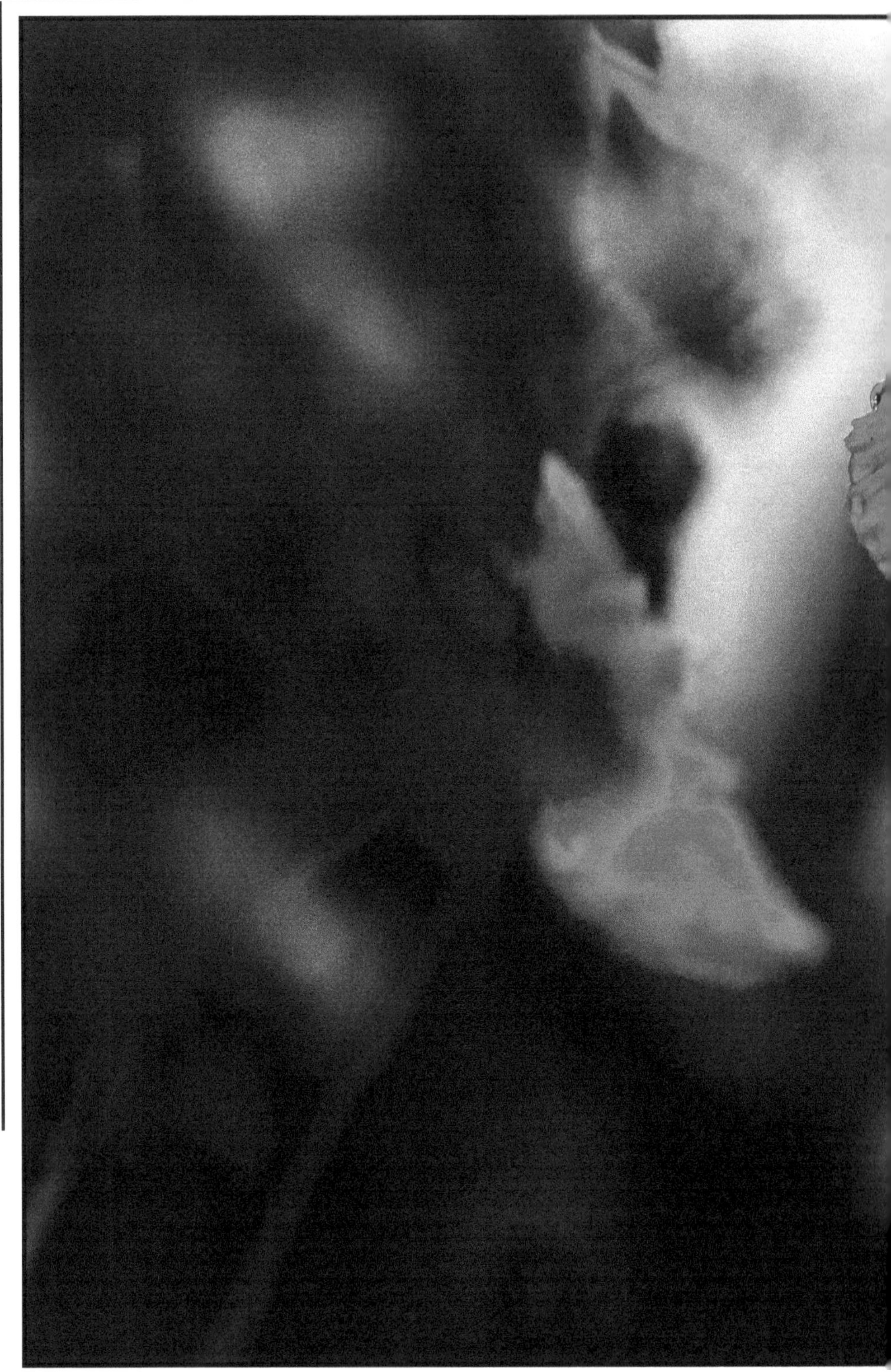

Ghazal for Getting Sober

Meara Levezow

We don't give up drinking forever-we can't. We decide to not pick up a drink *just for today*.
I will accept what is, I'll try to watch the train rush by without jumping, just for today.

This morning I opened my first e-mail sober. Tonight I'll try to shower without a beer.
We admitted we were powerless over alcohol. But I know I can't make it to the store today.

On our first date, I turn my will and my life over to the care of three quick shots of tequila
while you go to the bathroom. How could I say (again) that I wouldn't drink anymore today.

"Hi, my name is two long scrapes along your palms, blood under the fingernails of your left
hand, and a skinned knee. I'll be your Sunday morning mystery gore today".

After 23 years clean, Bobby got Vicodan for his shattered elbow, taken under a doctor's care.
He was still hitting the 12:30 meeting at St. Mary's every day. He would have been 54 today.

*Thousands of us wondered what we would do, once we stopped drinking, with all that time
on our hands*. I had off so I went to a meeting and spent another 6 hours in the bookstore today.

Chris the jazz guitarist told me that I wouldn't be able to sleep for months, so to just lie down
and rest my body at night. He seemed to intuit the volume of my addiction's roar today.

I look out the window. My addiction is out there in the parking lot doing push-ups, sweating on
the asphalt. Hi. I'm Meara I'm an alcoholic. I said that yesterday. Hi. I'm Meara. Encore: today.

Unjust Perspectives

Thomas Kneeland

—for Ahmaud Arbery

I'm sure he thought he'd never
have to fight for peace.
I'm sure he thought he'd never
have to die for peace.
And if there's one thing I've
learned about having big dreams,
it's that, even for a moment, the
trade-off is an unusually long
sleep.

So he's asleep now, dreaming among
the martyred souls—
the martyred souls who showed us
how important it is to love our own.

He can't come back now, until enough
of us have paid for peace with skin and
bullet blood-stained shirts for running
miles down the street.

Their perspectives didn't see
a black man of intelligence,

Their perspectives only
saw what hatred created.

Their perspectives didn't see
black boy gold,

Their perspectives saw a
colored nigga cold—

a cold-blooded murder on a Georgia street
after running two miles to his freedom beat.

Unlike Icarus who lost waxen wings when
he flew too close to the sun, my brother
gained busted cap and wings, the closer he
ran towards the son.

And the father was pleased
with what the son had done,
And the father was pleased
with what the son had done,
And the father was pleased with
what the son had done,
And when they were finally charged,
a mother still wept for her son.

The world in which we live
has a murderous rhyme—

kill this nigga, kill that
nigga and then we'll all be
fine.

How many more hashtags
will we create before we
change our perspective?

Social Media Hegemony

Lynn Tait

Love bombed in all the wrong news feeds
hacked identities forward messages: want you to share.
You've got 24 hours to lip sync a storm –
Tik tok, tik tok. *Un-friend, block, delete.*

Scrolling rivers of posts meant to inspire,
congratulations replaces kindness,
the opinionated chastised, emails, texts ignored,
tweet 280 characters of free speech or f-off,
instagram photos reach the usual twenty-five,

click on nightshade's shadow dance
lurking behind an unknown profile –
it's a mushy eggplant gif – no envy here, no *Haha, Wow.*

It's okay to suffer in cyberspace – all the memes say so;
anything that matters melting away on empty links.
Facebook heroes posting cats below caring emoticons,
all those *thumb ups* waiting to be born.

We're pickled pink, and on that sour note,
trolls corner the market on vinegar by the bin.
Spreading the virus everyone's searching for,
if cornered the sense of false news and YouTube videos
fills the airwaves — comments disabled.

Emoji hearts show up at odd hours, way past their bedtime.
I may know you beyond the keyboard, the avatar.
So I've built a fort out of poetry books.
Update myself lobbing lines, stanza and verse.

Long notes composed for *like/love* responses;
accused of leading an armchair life by *friends*,
beyond-reproach-ethics favour the intellectual muscle
behind the 'right' people thinking differently;
different people speaking up – how dangerous is that?

Social media hash tags itself – you're it!
There's a new Eggplant King smelling up the internet.

A Large Percentage of Missing Women Fit through Missing Women-shaped Cracks

Beth Dufford

even though, low carb or no,
  it may not fit your lifestyle

because no matter how little,
  no one wants to see them

because if you can't take a joke,
  I was only kidding

if the crack fits

because fat
  is fat free

if fat is free, why
  am I not?

if all women are
  good women

if a large percentage of missing women are missing

MACSTARLING

Jill Carpenter

Starlings, 100; America, 0

William Shakespeare (1564-1616) has been dead for more than 400 years. It's time for a mini-series, and I have a great idea that Ken Burns hasn't thought of. Yet.

The story spans two continents. It's an ark story. It's a Mayflower story. It has action, violence, imagination, ingenuity and adaptability. It involves common people, common birds, and state and federal agencies. Science and literature. Literature and science.

It's titled "MacStarling," and it all starts because a British playwright knew a hawk from a handsaw. Shakespeare started so many things, including that saying. He knew well the plant and animal species living around him, and he mentioned 57 different birds in his works. No one thought of redacting them. Why would they? Garden clubs love to create Shakespeare gardens.

The camera pans through the trees, and comes to rest, on the European starlings nesting in the thatched roof of Shakespeare's house at Stratford-Up-on-Avon. Inside, Shakespeare's wife spreads a canopy over the bed to catch the birds' droppings and the bugs they miss. Shakespeare is busily writing, thinking.

Birds chatter in the trees of the English countryside. They are known residents, and are happy where they are. The New World has been discovered, and Europeans are starting settlements there, but for the birds: Immigration never enters their minds.

Calendar pages flip quickly. Centuries pass. The late nineteenth century appears.

In New York City (show the New York World building; the Empire State building is still in the future), nattily dressed Eugene Schieffelin, a member of an old well-to-do Manhattan family, and an amateur ornithologist, lays down lays down a well-worn copy of *The Complete Works of William Shakespeare*, and sighs. He gazes out his apartment window into Central Park. A flock of pigeons noisily abandons his fire escape. He longs to hear a nightingale, a skylark, some higher-class British birds. On the wall behind him is his certificate of membership in the Acclimatization Society (no kidding). Thirty years before, he had sponsored the introduction of the house sparrow. They did well.

Schieffelin *could* visit Stratford-upon-Avon, but then he would always have to return home on one of those big ships, a long voyage without many birds, and besides, he gets seasick. Instead of going to the birds—Oh fateful day!—he decides to bring Shakespeare's birds to him. Shades of the future, a foreshadowing of Amazon.

The calendar stops on 1890. A noisy ship docks in New York harbor. Cages are unloaded. They contain birds, birds, birds: nightingales, bullfinches, chaffinches, European starlings. Sixty starlings to start with. (Show British bird-catchers, with nets, and robbing nests.) Another 40 starlings the next year.

Eugene enjoys their songs and chatters to them a bit before he accompanies them to Central Park and happily watches them fly away.

The birds are confused.

The fragile nightingales and skylarks and others, homesick for their familiar climate and food, eventually expire in the unfamiliar setting. Schieffelin sees fewer and fewer of them as he watches out his window. So much for that. Fun while it lasted.

The proletariat and sort-of-average starlings, however, have been around people for a long time. To them, a house is a house is a house. They make the best of things. Matter-of-factly, a pair builds a nest under the eaves of (show it) the American Museum of Natural History.

The birds ripple out from Central Park. Soon they are seen by Bostonians and Philadelphians (show Faneuil Hall, the Liberty Bell.). Their reproduction puts rabbits to shame.

Schieffelin dies in 1906. But he has set into motion a war. A war of two species.

People fire shotguns into the starlings' noisy roosting trees. (Audio: birds and shotgun blasts.)

(The calendar again, and a map.) Starlings cross the Mississippi before 1930.

People across the country douse the birds with fire hoses (physical force), spray them with soap (destroy their insulation), grease their roosting sites (so they will slip off).

People set off Roman candles, clang bells, slap boards together, fill balloons with dried peas and jiggle the balloons to make frightening hissing noises. (Lots of visual and audio opportunities; you choose.)

(More calendars, more maps.) In 1943, starlings reach Pullman, Washington.

In 1949, they are breeding in Salt Lake City.

Across the nation, scientific studies are commissioned. How to control the starling? (Scientists, in white lab coats, scratch their heads.) It is a bit late, like how to control the European immigration to the New World. How to control viruses. (There are many parallels.)

In 1952, a lone starling is spotted in Juneau, Alaska. No one can catch it.

Many dozens of Ph.D. dissertations and master's theses are written about starlings. Flocks of researchers write progress reports about starling control (show charts and graphs).

They are more obnoxious than house sparrows, who have learned to cluster around McDonald's and eat old French fries, and nest on the struts above the drive-throughs, and in traffic lights. (Visual.)

Starlings have learned that when in Rome, they can do as the Romans do. They probe in bark crevices like nuthatches, they hover at nectar feeders like hummingbirds, they brace themselves on tree trunks like woodpeckers, they forage at the edge of busy highways. They peek like elf owls from holes in saguaro cacti. (Visuals abound here.)

They are sociable and like flocks, and sometimes join native blackbirds in their swooping flights and roosts.

They were pre-adapted, and they are adaptable. Like another species we know well.

(Conclusion: Zoom in to me at the computer, typing. Or I could be looking at a picture of a starling, which has beautiful iridescent feathers. It could be next to a genealogical chart of my ancestors, who go back to William the Conqueror, 1066.)

More than 400 years after Shakespeare was born far across the Atlantic Ocean, more than 200 million starlings are residing in the United States.

Inspiring its literature.

10 Social Isolation Games

Gavin Boyter

1. CURVE: Take an item of household furniture and saw it into pieces approxi mately 12 inches by 8 inches square. Whittle or carve these pieces into rounded, flat, chevron shapes. After carving each piece, take it into the garden (open a window if you live in a city). Hurl each piece into the sky, imparting a rapid spin. Some of the objects may return, after describing a giant curve; others will not. Teeth may be lost, windows endangered. In the interests of charity, you may wish to write encouraging messages upon each missile: take heart, hope springs eternal, help is coming.

2. ANATOMY: Label each part of your body with its function with a black marker pen. Give each part a mark out of ten depending on how much you like and need it. Make sure your assessment is honest and accurate. This will help when playing game seven. It may help to remember some of the uses you previously put these body parts to. Arms were once used for hug ging, hands for stroking the hair of others. Feet once walked along beaches or climbed rugged hillsides. Do you really need more than one hand? What is your penis actually for?

3. POETRY: Find all the rhymes for coronavirus, glad you named your first child Cyrus. Should we all work until they fire us? What if no one else will hire us? All these strictures serve to tire us, reprogram us, restart, rewire us. Will our future kids admire us if we let the thick mud mire us? If of hope you are desirous, in the grey matter 'tween each gyrus, lurks a thought that might inspire us. Write it quickly on papyrus! Alas, this battle may require us to trample down the purple iris, on the road to meet Osiris.

4. CONSPIRACY: find as many people to blame as humanly possible for the situation you find yourself in. This game is best played by one player alone. It will help if you are the President of the United States and a massive narcissist forced by the weight of the entire world's suffering to realise both your innate inadequacy and fundamental inconsequentiality, along with the fact that you have been handed the most poisoned of chalices and required to drink. Sup deep, sociopath! Feel the frothy poison calcify in your fat-deadened arteries. This is not fake news, this is ineluctable truth.

5. AFTERLIFE: List all the things you plan to do when the strictures are finally lifted. Visit the Great Wall of China, play badminton with your cousin Adam, finally talk to the pretty girl in the coffee shop, start running again, wear livelier and more colourful clothes, call your parents at least once a week, shop for presents for all the friends you missed desperately during the Lockdown Spring. Plaster the garden wall. Take up windsurfing. Learn

mandarin. Climb Mount Kilimanjaro. Dance with a real live Brazilian. Drink absinthe. Will you finally learn to play the piano? You will not.

6. BLOODTHIRSTY: You have long been aware that black pudding is basically just oatmeal, and congealed pig's blood. There is an awful lot of oatmeal sitting in that high cupboard berating you for not being able to like porridge. There is a surprising amount of blood in the human body. YouTube can supply a How To video for almost anything – why not self-cannulation? As a vegetarian, you can't have a moral objection to consuming your own blood, can you? Is there really any need to inform the other members of your family what they are eating? I don't think so.

7. DISMEMBERMENT: Just hangs there, being pretty redundant, and by that, I mean not at all pretty. It's just a fleshy tube, really. You hardly even bother getting it "excited" anymore. If it wasn't there, you would still be able to pee, and your trousers would fit better. You might even be able to wear Speedos without embarrassment. Hell, you could even wear your wife's bikini bottoms at a pinch. It's not as if you were going to have any more kids, anyway. Hair straighteners could be repurposed as a cauterising device. I wonder what it would taste like, sautéed?

8. CONTINENTAL: Declare part of your home is another continent and set up a toll. You needn't collect money for passing through the checkpoint. Any item of worth, special favour or shameful enactment might suffice. This way, you can ensure social distancing, whilst shoring up your own reserves of toilet paper, flour and entertaining memories of the self-abasement of those you love. However, unless you can recruit other family members to work shifts with you, you may find border encroachments become rife. There is only one punishment for such foolhardiness, isn't there, and you know just what must be done.

9. SENTINEL: Stand in the middle of your street at night, with face upturned. Let the stars bear witness as you declare: I am the sentinel and I watch the road. I am the sentinel, and none shall pass. I am the sentinel; I bear witness to the end of days at last. I am the sentinel, on my shoulders, rests the weight of future days, I am the sentinel, growing older, burnished by the summer's blaze. I am the sentinel, ceremonial, to the ghosts who pass away. I am the sentinel, testimonial, for other ghosts who come to stay.

10. GUEST: Go to the house of another and look in his windows. Hold up a placard: "give me shelter; I am homeless". You will be allowed into the home of this good Samaritan. Take off your clothes and hand your host a piece of chalk. Tell them to draw a pentagram and ask for five candles. Write sacred symbols inside each of the five points. Lie down in the centre of the pentagram, light the candles and turn off all the lights. Offer the blade handle first. If your host blanches, you may have to do the bloodletting yourself.

True Facts About the Ancient American Indian as Told by Pop Culture, History Textbooks, and the Internet: A helpful compilation for the White Man.

Leah Myers

Every Indian is good at basketball.

> *Note: Any Indian that claims otherwise is trying to trick you, be wary.*

Being an Indian is race and religion bundled into one.

> *Note: For those confused, think of it as a "buy one, get one free" deal on oppression.*

Every Indian is connected to nature
and all speak to animals regularly.

> *Note: Many have reported the customary greeting when communing with spirits translates roughly to "Beware the White Man" but this has yet to be confirmed.*

Every Indian owns a headdress
and loves to watch white people wear them.

> *Note: What looks like anger in their eyes is likely jealousy that you are wearing it better. Release a hand-over-mouth war cry to let them know you still respect where they came from.*

Team names like the Chiefs and the Redskins
honor the fallen warriors of the past.

> *Note: If an Indian is upset at the use of these words, remind them who holds the modern scalping knife of institutionalized discrimina tion. They will be quieted.*

Indians love to hear white people
use the word "Indian."

> *Note: Native American or indigenous may sound more respectful, but stick with your gut. If they can say it, why can't you?*

They are red because they are demons
that are soaked in the blood of the white man.

Note: If an Indian appears to have a natural skin tone, they have merely enchanted your eyes, rewatch old cartoons such as Peter Pan for reference.

All Indians are alcoholics.
Their livers are steely and worth nearly as much as their scalps.

Note: Using this as an advantage will also make you seem more be lievable when your story is compared to the Drunk Indian's tale.

Every single Indian has diabetes
or small pox.

Note: Both will kill them, be patient.

90% of the Indians mysteriously vanished
shortly after the arrival of guns and germs.

Note: Don't take back the blankets.

Today, all Indians are old, selling frybread by the road,
or dead with an unmarked grave.

Note: You can bulldoze either without a flinch from the government, just do so quietly in the name of progress.

Dreams and Memories

Andrea Lewicki

Better Place or Just a Better Way to Fall

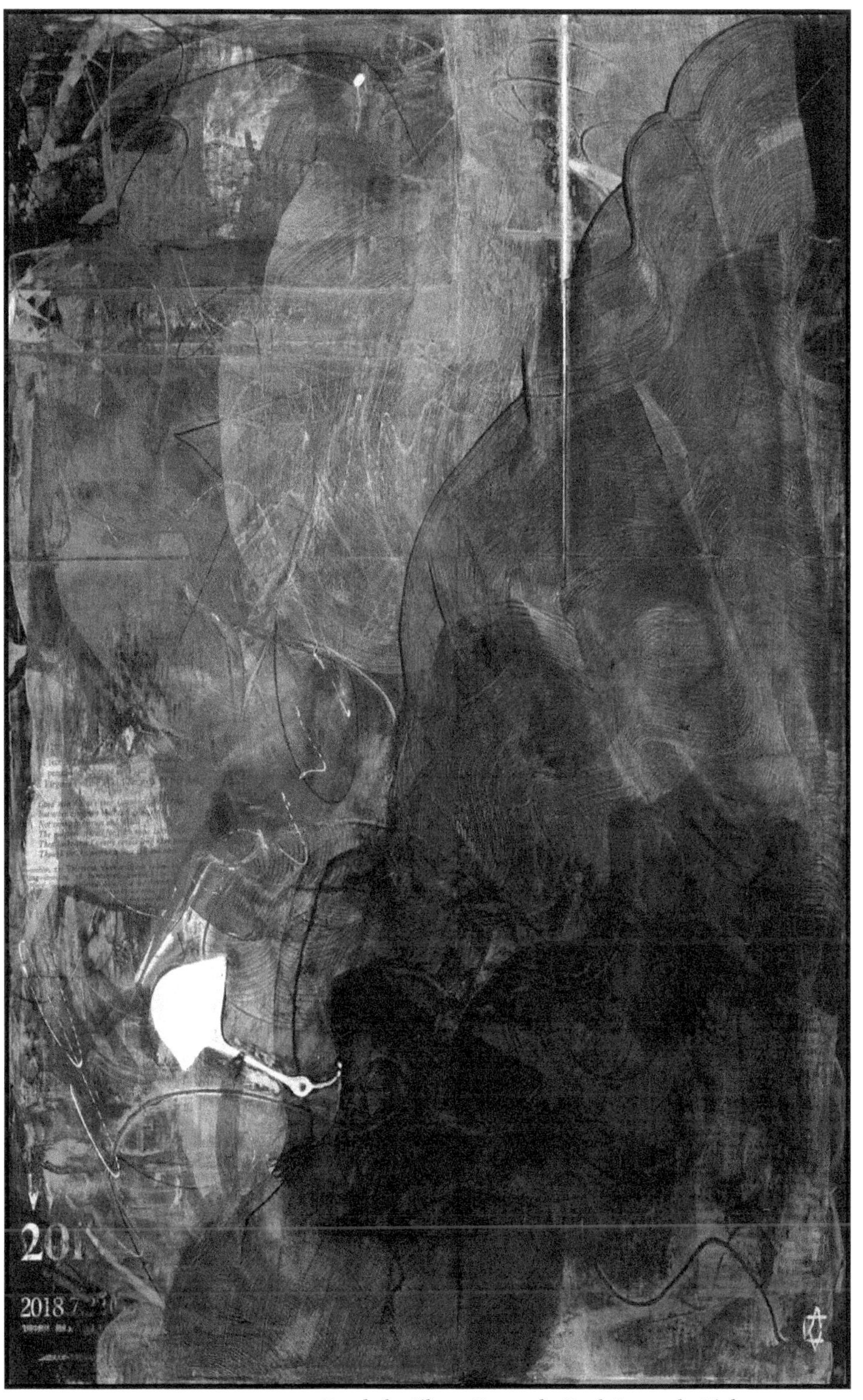

Break the Silence Damn the Dark Damn the Light

Here I Come Square One

Square One Here I Come

You Dress Up for Armageddon I Dress Up for Summer

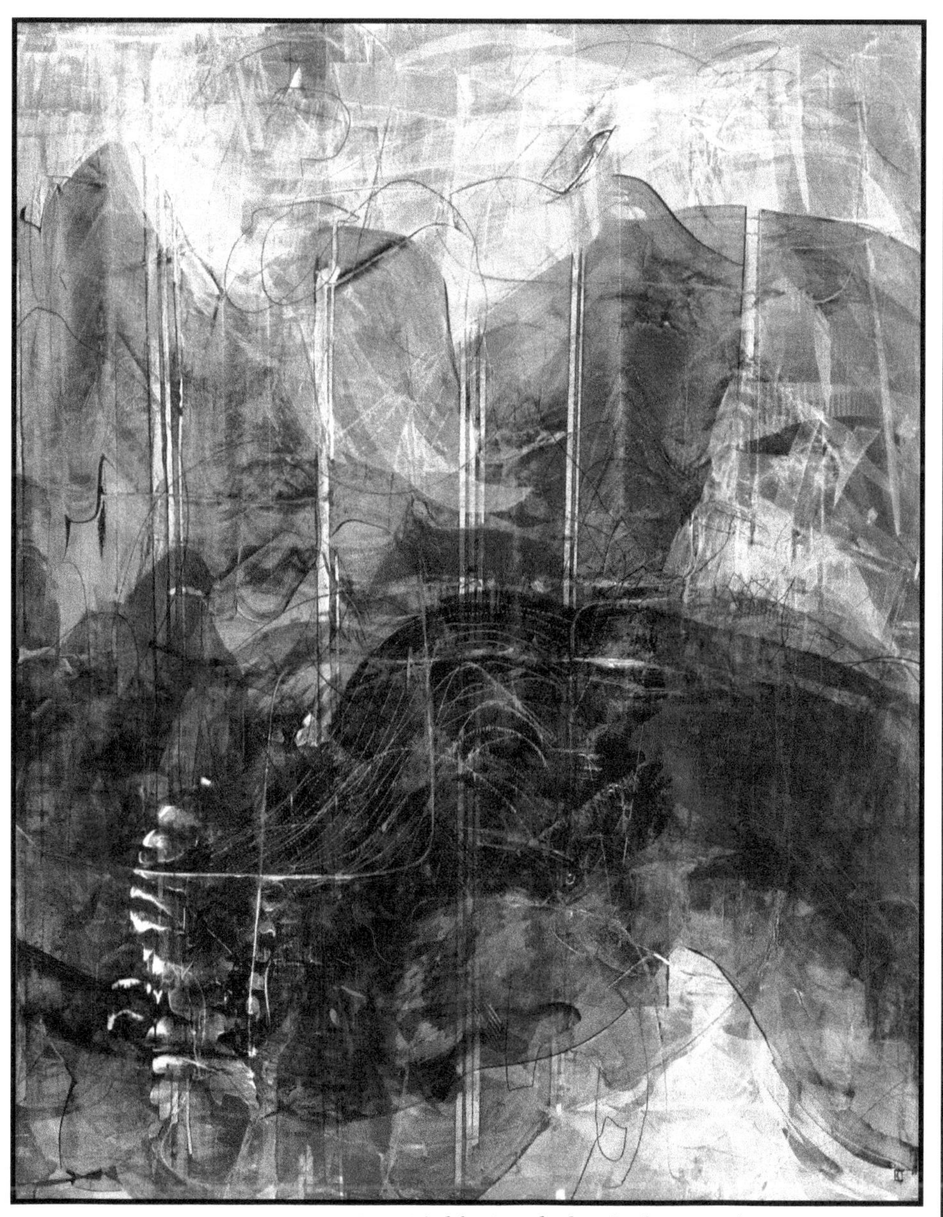

Jesus Died for Somebodys Sins but Not Mine

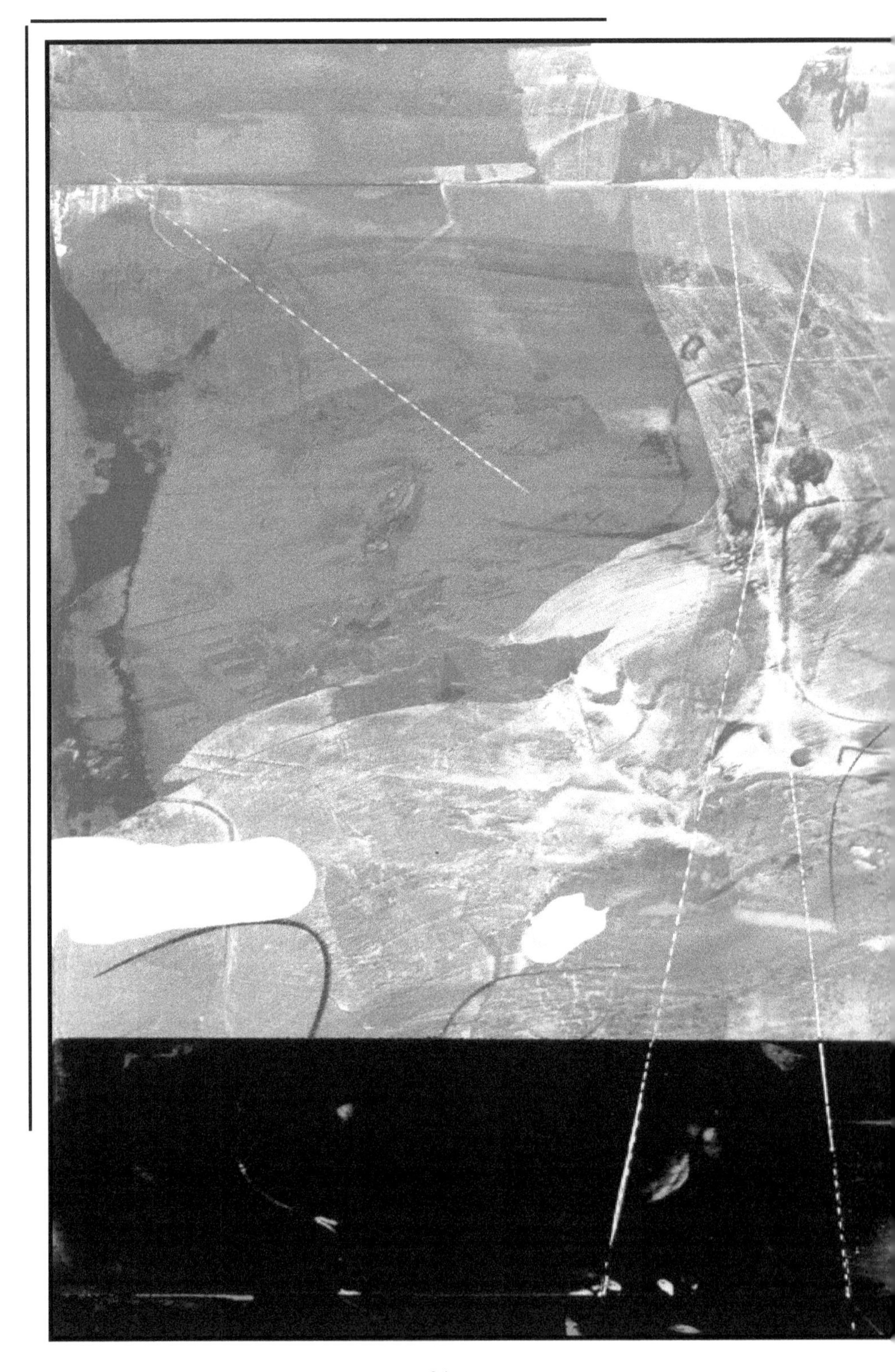

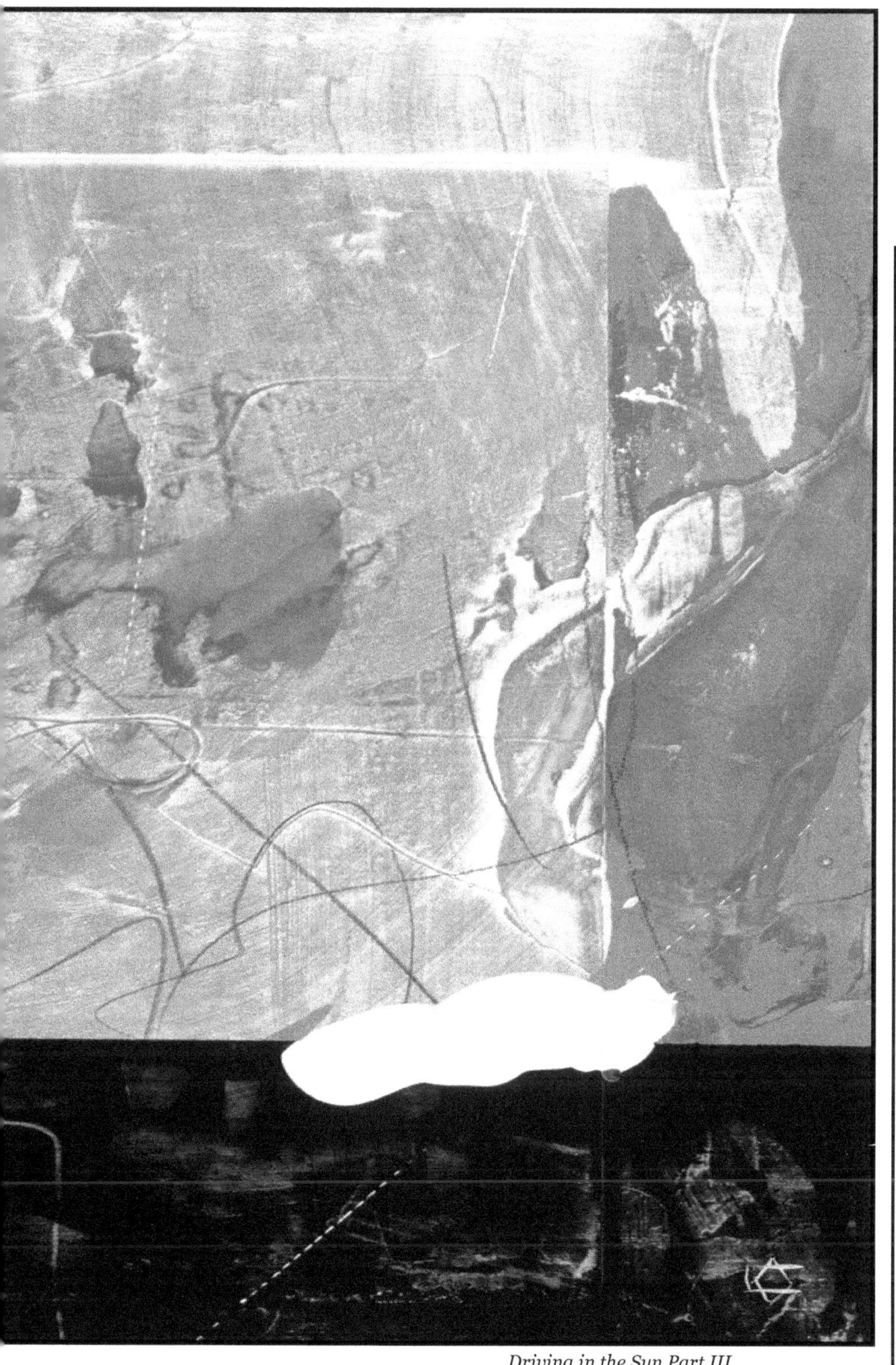

Driving in the Sun Part III

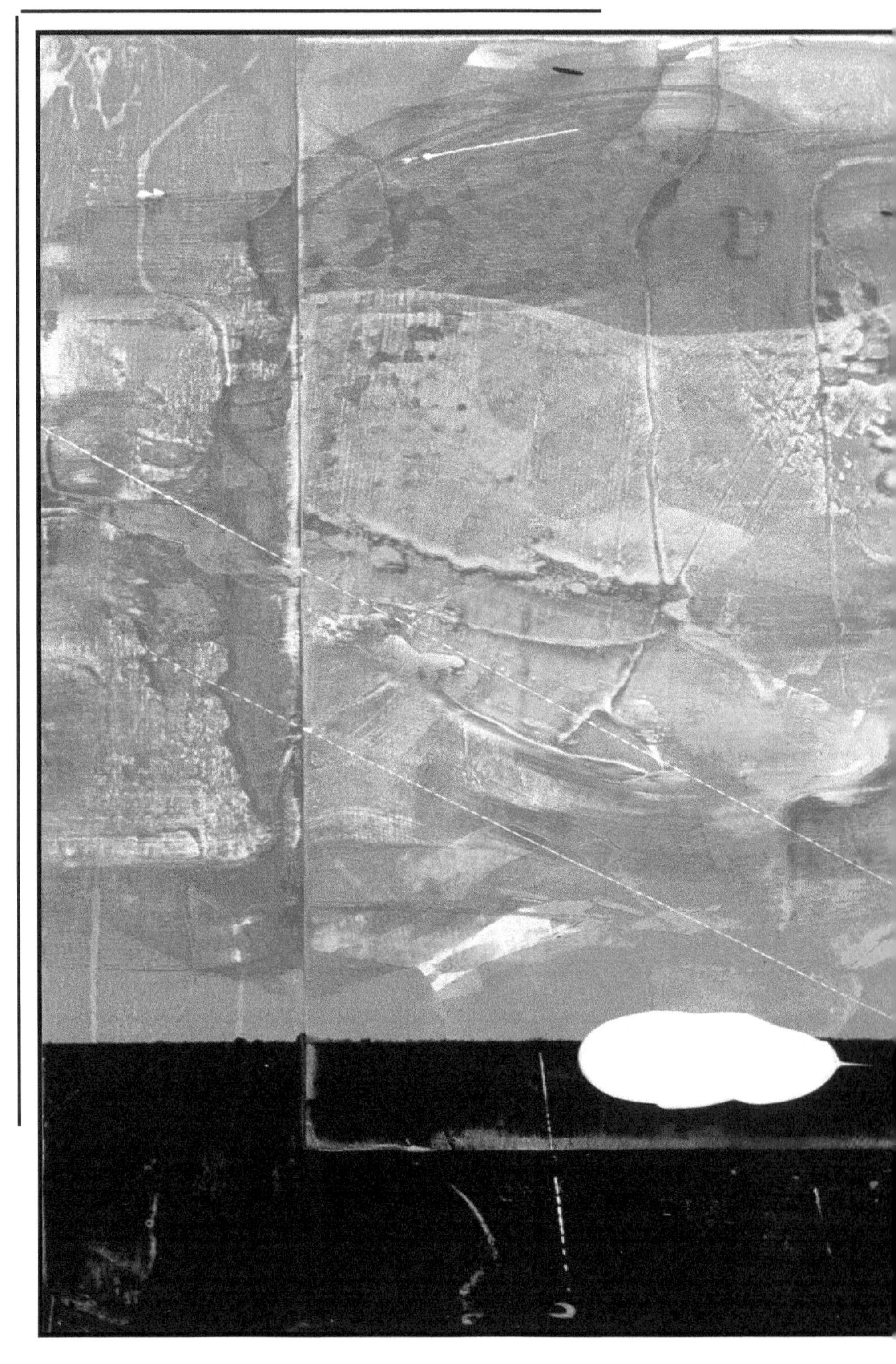

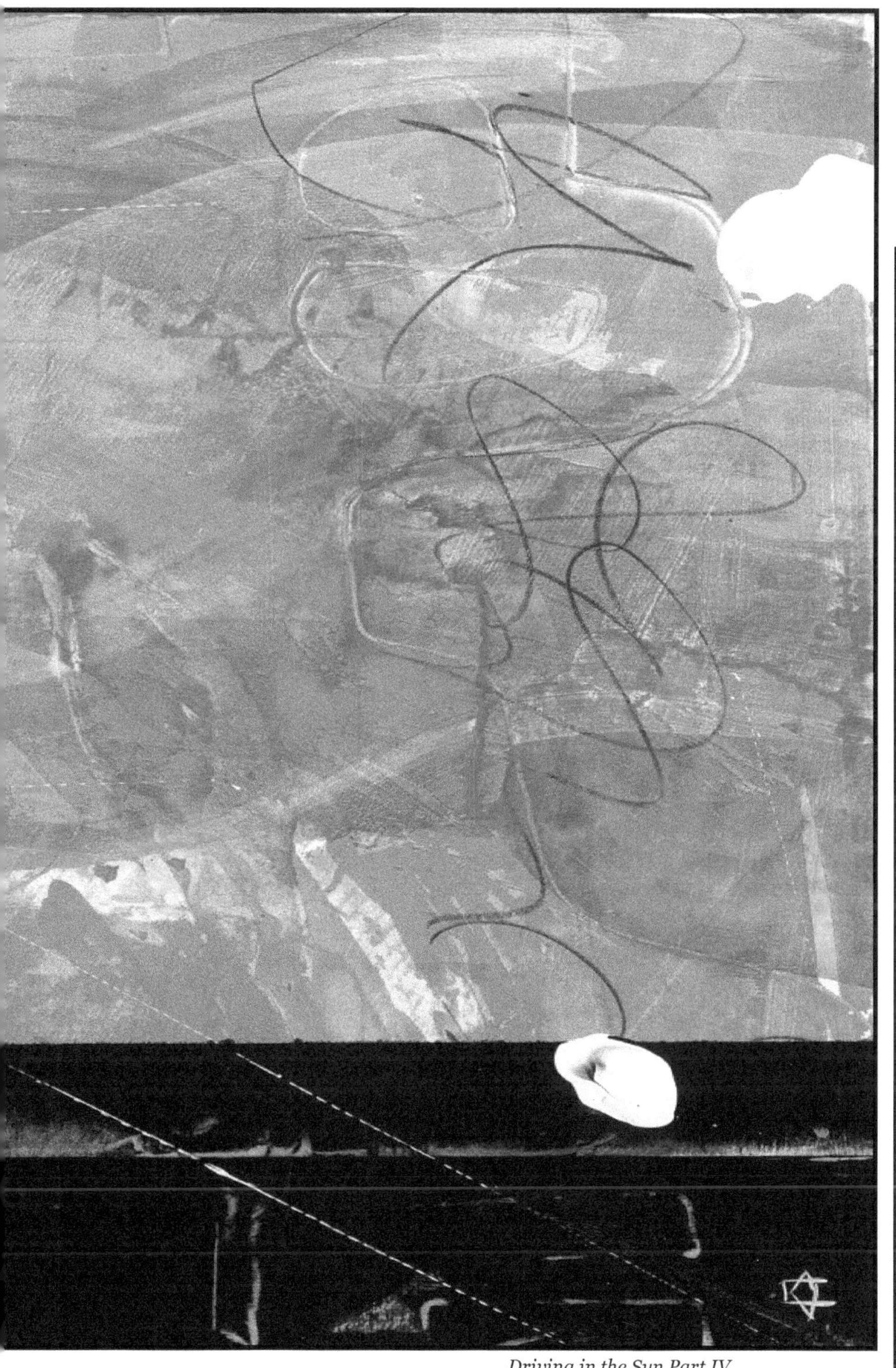

Driving in the Sun Part IV

the seed crown

Photography by Kristen Herrington & Lyndsay Doyle

Poetry by Elise Scott

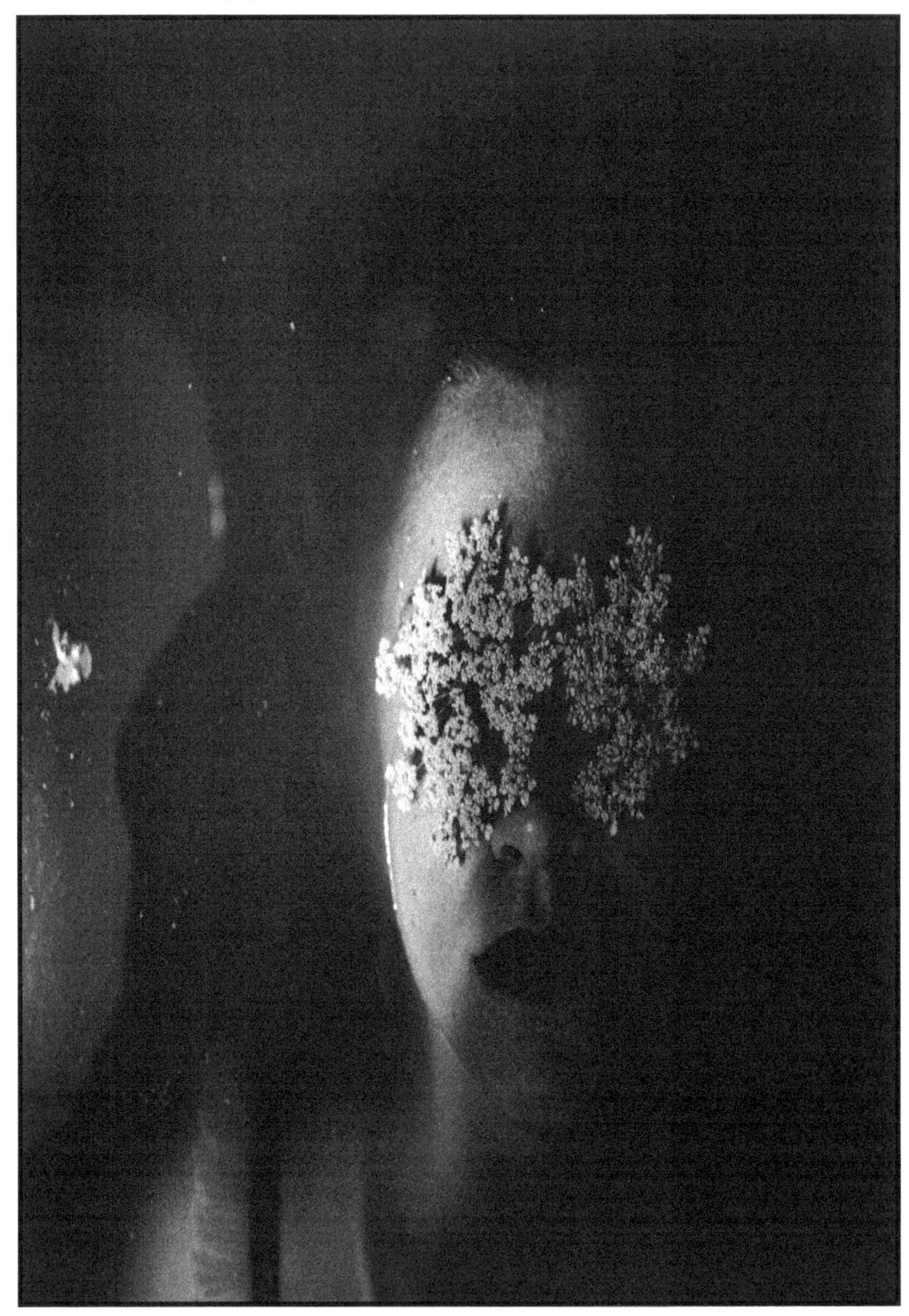

because of this thing that just happened,
i want the finest knife.
i want to reach the core with one
clean stroke. the seeds do not interest me.
what i want is to lift out those crisp shells
that guard the arsenic, and the blueprints
of furrowed leaves to come.
i want to build you a crown of them.
it will pearlesce and smell faintly
of an orchard.

i find myself humming with
the peculiar quavering shame of the voyeur.
behind your altar is a cigar box, cupping
dusty magic like an antique cradle.
an earring, a superhero, a seed. also,
innumerable scraps of paper, each
with the word love on it. the traceries
of your fluid hand
sketching her in the air,
more exquisite than she ever was.
more exquisite than i am.

you ripped apart *almost* to find a kernel
ephemeral enough to dip
your quill into. you thought
your poet soul so generous, and
buried the leftover bones & scraps
under our bed, drunk
on the silent despair of
it all. you're doing it again, etching
false scars over virgin
skin, pouring
words like libations to make
a belt or a bottlecap
sacred.
you, craving your *alone.* I stare
at the ink pouring from your forehead.

i wish
i were good enough
to wish you had loved her better.

In Order Of Appearance:

A graduate of the University of Lynchburg, C. Hiatt O'Connor was the former Co-Head Editor in Chief of the University's literary magazine, the PRISM, and has received multiple honors for his poetry, including: the Libbie Keaton LaPrade writing award; the Belle M. Hill creative poetry award; and the Miriam T. & Jude Pfister prize from the Academy of American Poets. He is published in The PRISM, The Allegheny Review, the Tiny Seed Literary Journal, and by The Academy of American Poets. He lives and works on a farm in Maryland.

Madeline Ewanyshyn is a Canadian writer who works at a library. In 2019, she graduated with a BA in Creative Writing from Kwantlen Polytechnic University. She has been published in literary magazines including The Liar, pulpMAG, Sea to Sky Review, The Opal Club, and The Lyre. She is currently working on her first novel.

Cleo Lockhart is an 18-year-old living in Denver, Colorado. A couple of her previous publications include Rare Byrd Review and the 2019 Bow Seat Yearbook. She can be found on Instagram at @ clock.hart.

Yaara is an Israeli photographer and 'slow travel' blogger currently living and working in France. As a traveler who specializes in culture-focused, in-depth trips to less-traveled destinations, the past few years of her life were dedicated to travel photography and she is continuously creating personal and commercial projects.

Charise M. Hoge, MA, MSW, is a dance/movement therapist, performing artist, and writer. Her work in arts and healing has brought wellness programs into hospitals, counseling centers, museums, and businesses. Her poetry has been published in These Fragile Lilacs Poetry Journal, The New Verse News, Tuck Magazine, High Shelf Press, Ulalume Lighthouse, Tiny Seed Literary Journal, "Next Line, Please" column of The American Scholar, the book Next Line, Please: Prompts to Inspire Poets and Writers (Cornell University Press, 2018) as well as her chapbook Striking Light from Ashes (Finishing Line Press, 2017). She has given poetry readings in a variety of venues, including: a gym, a meditation center, an arts festival, a dance performance, and on a moving streetcar for Art All Night DC. @charhogepoet

Native of Boston and Martha's Vineyard, MA., Stelios Mormoris has been a marketing executive in the beauty industry, having worked for L'Oréal, Yves Rocher and COTY. He currently is the CEO of a new company, EDGE BEAUTY, Inc., which markets wellness products online. A dual citizen of Greece and the United States, and raised in New York, Stelios has spent most of his adult life living in Paris. He received his undergraduate degree in architecture at Princeton, and M.B.A. from INSEAD in Paris.
Stelios is a former professional rugby player, having played for the Ligue Bayonne. He is also a contemporary artist, and specializes in abstract oil painting [www.steliosmormoris.com]. Stelios was part of the Creative Writing Program at PRINCETON, and student of William Meredith and Maxine Kumin, and later at COLUMBIA with Stanley Kunitz, and David Ignatow, and with the ACADEMY OF AMERICAN POETS with Nancy Schoenberger.
He has published work in VERSE, PRESS, the WHELK WALK REVIEW, GARGOYLE, SPILLWAY, the NASSAU LITERARY REVIEW, SPILLWAY, SUGAR HOUSE REVIEW, MIDWEST POETRY REVIEW, SOUTH ROAD, and other literary journals.
Stelios has held positions on the Boards of the French Cultural Center of BOSTON, Historic New England, the Fragrance Foundation, SYMRISE, S.A., and ACT-UP, and the Kytherian Society.

Phoebe Greer is a secular Jewish writer living in New York, NY. While attending LIU Global, Phoebe earned a BA in Global Studies and Creative Writing. Phoebe has appeared in the Bangalore Mirror and been a featured reader in India's Poetry Across Borders reading series. Phoebe was a finalist for a Brooklyn Poets fellowship, has read at the Poetry Project and been published in their online journal, The Recluse.

Bill Schulz lives in Windham, Maine. He is a poet, photographer, and manic doodler. His poetry and artwork have appeared in may periodicals over the past 40 years, including The Aurorean, High Shelf, Seneca Review, and Nine Mile.

Gwen Bernick is a sophomore at The College of New Jersey studying English and Philosophy. She works as a cog in the capitalist machine at a major big-box store, and tries to make her life meaningful outside of productivity with philosophical pursuits and poetry. Her work has also appeared in the Kelsey Review.

Catherine LeComte is a Boston based photographer, specializing in fine art and portrait photography. She holds a BFA in Photography, acquired from the Savannah College of Art and Design in 2014. Shrtly after graduating, she set off to spend four years traveling and photographing in Asia. Her work has been published and exhibited both abroad and within the United States.

Jessica Bidwell: I am a transitioning veteran; over the last decade I spent my time globe trotting with the Navy. One constant, my camera was never far from reach. I was blessed with the opportunity to capture moments that would forever inform, teach and reach future generations, offering a muse to serve or simply a glimpse of the world from a Sailor's perspective.
As I immerse myself in the civilian sector, one thing remains the same, I constantly find myself behind the lens capturing frames with the desire that others will be as inspired as I am by merely a moment in time.
I am currently rediscovering America from behind the lens compiling a portfolio highlighting aspects of nature that we, too often, overlook. I fear that our minds are so consumed with the day-to-day that we often miss the beauty that lies just before us. This consumption is at no fault of our own; rather, it is symptom of our society. If more persons were to lust in the beauty which surrounds us, then, maybe, we would all be more motivated to preserve it.
Home based in Denver, Colorado. I have 15 years of experience, a degree in portrait and commercial photography and I attended the Military Visual Journalism program at Syracuse University's Newhouse School of Public Communication.
Website: www.jblynnstudio.com

Meara Levezow is a queer poet from Sheboygan, Wisconsin living in Brooklyn. Her work has appeared or is forthcoming in Bluestem Magazine, The Inkwell Journal, and The Midwest Review, among others. She has worked in restaurants for over twenty years.

Thomas Kneeland is the author of two collections of poetry -- "Shades of Gold" (2018) and "Uncaged: Breathing in Public" (2019) -- and a chapbook entitled, "Injusticed League: Dark Matters" (2020). Thomas is the Founder & Executive Director of The Kneeland Center for Poetry, Inc., a 501c3 nonprofit that discovers, cultivates, and enhances the voices and works of underrepresented poets. Additionally, Thomas is the Editor-in-Chief for the nonprofit's online poetry journal, The Elevation Review, which just released its inaugural issue on August 17, 2020.
Thomas was recently published in Up the Staircase Quarterly's 50th Issue on August 1st.

Lynn Tait is an award-winning poet/photographer living in Sarnia Ontario. Her poetry has appeared in Contemporary Verse 2, Windsor Review, Vallum, FreeFall Literary Magazine, Literary Review of Canada and in over 100 North American anthologies. Her photo art has graced the cover of seven books of poetry. She is a member of The Ontario Poetry Society and the League of Canadian Poets.

Beth Dufford lives, works, and writes in Kerhonkson, NY and sometimes New York City. Her work has appeared in Barrow Street, The Little Magazine, Rise Up Review, Common Ground Review, and Crab Creek Review. Her chapbook, Microscopic Peaceful Implosions, was published in May 2018 by Eyewear Publishing.

Jill Carpenter has worked as a science writer, college instructor, and book seller. After 30 years in the South, she has retired to Tucson, AZ, where she went to university. She is writing poems about scientists about whom she intended to write biographies.

Gavin Boyter: I am a Scottish writer and filmmaker living in London. I have published two travel memoirs about running ludicrously long distances, Downhill from Here and Running the Orient. The latter book charts my 2300 mile run from Paris to Istanbul, following the 1883 route of the Orient

Express. My stories have been published in Constellations, Blueing the Blade, DIAGRAM, Riptide, The Closed Eye Open, Bright Flash, La Piccioletta Barca, Every Day Fiction and The Abstract Elephant. I am also the writer-director of the 2015 independent film Sparks and Embers.

Leah Myers is a Native American writer with roots in Georgia, Arizona, and Washington, and is currently pursuing an MFA in Creative Nonfiction at the University of New Orleans. Her work has previously appeared in Spillers No.7, RED INK: International, and Newfound. Leah is a member of the Jamestown S'Klallam Tribe and can be found on both Instagram and Twitter under @n8v_wordsmith.

Andrea Lewicki is a mostly self-taught abstract artist, fueled by persistent curiosity. She describes her art world as a place where nothing is obvious, straight-on, or predictably duplicated. Although she was nearly 30 years old when she met an artist for the first time, she grew up surrounded by people who made their living with their hands. This carries through into the studio where she paints without brushes, invents her own painting tools, and explores the physical nature of her materials. Lewicki works in a rhythm of alternating divergent and convergent processes, often building up a visual language through rapid improvisation before breaking through the emergent structure with slow deliberation. She sands, scrapes, and peels through layers, and prioritizes the tactile quality of her pieces as much as the visual content.
Lewicki lives in Western Washington's Snoqualmie Valley.

Though born and raised in a small farming community in rural Nova Scotia, Kristen Herrington has called Halifax home for more than a decade. She is a prolific abstract painter and designer, with a particular interest in collaborative works. She studied -what she calls- the artist's "thing" for her Master's thesis as an avenue to explore the relationship between the creative individual working in a capitalist society. Through this research, Kristen discovered her own "thing" and has been working on that artistic evolution for the past 6 years.
She identifies as a fluid-artist, capturing life's overlooked moments or ideas on her canvasses. Additionally, she explores the raw and vulnerable nature of the female form. She has worked as a nude model for her local arts university and has recently collaborated with her photography friend and co-collaborator, Lyndsay Doyle to bring a gritty take on her "other" personality.

After a decade in the corporate world, Lyndsay made the leap to full-time entrepreneurship in 2012 so she could make her own rules. With a headstrong and quirky personality, Lyndsay approaches her work in a straightforward way, taking care to relay strong social messages with her art through humour and honesty. Her photography and writing clearly show her passion for social justice issues, particularly in the field of women's rights. Whether through subject-based projects, or through self-portraiture, she weaves art, business, and audience interaction seamlessly, while focussing on projects that specifically aim to break down barriers for women, celebrate their strengths, and create discussion.

Elise is an adventurous, queer earth-mother in a wheelchair and an enthusiastic vegan cheese-maker. She writes from her lived experiences of mental illness & physical disability, pansexuality, and shouting at ghosts. Elise's checkered past includes project and team management, educator training throughout New England, and counseling at-risk youth in Boston with the aid of an inordinately large sub-woofer. She is currently a full-time writer/mom in Connecticut, where she live with one tiny daughter and over three hundred pounds of fur-family.

Highshelfpress.com